WITHDRAWN

MAY 14 1963

PRICE LIST - SALE 2193 - OLD MASTERS FROM THE CINTAS COLLECTION
PARKE-BERNET GALLERIES INC - MAY 1, 1963 - 8:00 P M

Lot	Price	Lot	Price
1	$2,000.00	13	$80,000.00
2	13,000.00	14	65,000.00
3	4,000.00	15	27,500.00
4	4,000.00	16	5,000.00
5	5,500.00	17	25,000.00
6	22,500.00	18	3,000.00
7	25,000.00	19	8,000.00
8	22,000.00	20	2,500.00
9	12,500.00	21	24,000.00
10	600,000.00	22	19,500.00
11	27,500.00	23	8,000.00
12	260,000.00	24	15,000.00

TOTAL - $1,280,000.00

THE MERRY LUTE PLAYER

HALS

Old Master Paintings

FROM THE COLLECTION OF THE LATE

Oscar B. Cintas

PUBLIC AUCTION

Wednesday Evening · May 1 at 8 o'clock

[Admission to Sale by Card Only]

Following Public Exhibition

from Friday · April 26

PARKE-BERNET GALLERIES · INC

New York · 1963

SALE NUMBER 2093

FREE PUBLIC EXHIBITION
Friday and Saturday, April 26 and 27 from 10 to 5
[Galleries Closed Sunday and Monday]

Tuesday, April 30 from 10 a. m. to 8 p. m.
[No Exhibition on Day of Sale]

PUBLIC AUCTION SALE
Wednesday Evening
May 1 at 8 o'clock

ADMISSION TO SALE BY CARD ONLY
To be obtained by application to the Galleries

EXHIBITION AND SALE AT THE
PARKE-BERNET GALLERIES · INC
980 Madison Avenue - 76th to 77th Street
NEW YORK 21

TRAFALGAR 9-8300   CABLE: PARKGAL

✦ ✦ ✦

Sales Conducted by

LOUIS J. MARION
WILLIAM A. SMYTH · THEODORE J. MULDOON
CHARLES A. HELLMICH · JOHN L. MARION

1963

BIOGRAPHICAL MEMOIR

OSCAR B. CINTAS (1887-1957) *sugar and railroad magnate and Cuban Ambassador to the United States in 1932-34, a great friend and admirer of America, was well known in art circles here and abroad as a passionate collector of paintings. All through his vigorous life he was interested in art; and over the years he assembled with discriminating taste a group of old masters which contained major examples of both the European and American schools, some of which were shown at the New York World's Fair in 1939-40.*

His purchases also included the earliest life portrait of Abraham Lincoln, which was given (as he would have wished) to the Chicago Historical Society, and one of the original manuscripts of the Gettysburg Address, presented to the United States and now on exhibition in the Lincoln Room of the White House.

Shortly before his death in 1957, and upon his instructions, a Foundation was formed under the laws of New York for the purpose of fostering art and providing fellowships for qualified artists of Cuban lineage. To this Foundation, Oscar Cintas left his collection of paintings in New York. In order to carry out the programme envisioned in the Foundation's charter, funds are needed. To obtain them, a sale of some of the paintings from the collection has become necessary.

The Parke-Bernet Galleries

will execute your bids without charge
if you are unable to attend the sale in person

Telephone: Trafalgar 9-8300
Cable: Parkgal

CONDITIONS OF SALE

The property listed in this catalogue will be offered and sold on the following terms and conditions:

1. The word "Galleries," whenever here used, means the Parke-Bernet Galleries, Inc.

2. The Galleries has endeavored to catalogue and describe the property correctly, but all property is sold "as is" and neither the Galleries nor its consignor warrants or represents, and they shall in no event be responsible for, the correctness of description, genuineness, authorship, provenience or condition of the property, and no statement contained in the catalogue or made orally at the sale or elsewhere shall be deemed to be such a warranty or representation, or an assumption of liability.

3. Unless otherwise announced by the auctioneer at the time of sale, all bids are to be for a single article even though more than one article is included under a numbered item in the catalogue. If, however, all of the articles under a numbered item are either specifically designated by the auctioneer at the time of the sale or designated in the printed catalogue as a "Lot," then bids are to be for the lot irrespective of the number of items. However, in book catalogues, *all* bids are to be for the lot as numbered, unless specific notification to the contrary is given by the auctioneer at the time of sale.

4. The highest bidder acknowledged by the auctioneer shall be the purchaser. In the event of any dispute between bidders, the auctioneer shall have absolute discretion either to determine the successful bidder, in which event his determination shall be final, or to re-offer and resell the article in dispute. If any dispute arises after the sale, the Galleries' sale record shall be conclusive as to who was the purchaser, the amount of the highest bid, and in all other respects.

5. If, the auctioneer, in his sole and final discretion, decides that any original bid is not commensurate with the value of the article offered, or, having acknowledged an original bid, that any advance thereafter is not of sufficient amount, he may reject the same.

6. The name and address of the purchaser of each article or lot shall be given to the Galleries immediately following the sale thereof, and payment of the whole purchase price, or such part thereof as the Galleries may require, shall be made immediately by the purchaser. If the foregoing condition, or any other applicable condition herein, is not complied with, the sale may, at the option of the Galleries, be cancelled and the article or lot re-offered for sale.

7. Unless the sale is advertised and announced as an unrestricted sale, or as a sale without reserve, the consignor has reserved the right to bid personally or by agent; and if the consignor or his agent is the highest bidder, less than full commissions may be payable.

8. Except as otherwise provided in paragraph 6 hereof, title will pass to the highest bidder upon the fall of the auctioneer's hammer, and thereafter, the purchaser shall bear the sole risk and responsibility for the property.

9. All property purchased is to be paid for in full and removed from the Galleries at the purchaser's risk and expense immediately after the conclusion of the sale. As to any property not so paid for in full, in addition to all other remedies available to the Galleries by law, including, without limitation, the right to hold the purchaser

liable for the bid price, the Galleries, at its option, may either (a) cancel the sale, in which event all payments made by the purchaser shall be retained as liquidated damages, or (b) resell the same without notice to the purchaser and for the purchaser's account and risk, either publicly or privately, and, in such event, the purchaser shall be liable for the payment of any deficiency plus all costs, including warehousing, the expenses of both sales, and the Galleries' commissions at its regular rates. All property not promptly removed by the purchaser, may be removed by the Galleries to a warehouse for the account and risk and at the expense of the purchaser.

10. Items or categories in this catalogue which are subject to the Federal Excise Tax on jewelry, clocks, silver, gold, furs, etc., are designated by an asterisk (*). Unless acquired by a registered dealer for resale, the purchaser will be required to pay in addition to the amount of his bid, the Federal Excise Tax equivalent to 10 per cent of the bid.

11. Unless exempt from the payment thereof, the purchaser will also be required to pay the New York City sales tax of 3 per cent of the bid.

12. The Galleries, without charge for its services, may undertake to make bids on behalf of responsible persons approved by it, including the consignor, subject to the Conditions of Sale and to such other terms and conditions as it may prescribe. The Galleries reserves the right, however, to decline to undertake to make such bids and when undertaking to make such bids shall in no event be responsible for failing correctly to carry out instructions.

13. The Galleries, at the purchaser's risk and expense, will facilitate the employment of carriers and packers for the purchaser's account, but will not be responsible for their acts in any respect whatsoever.

14. Any and all claims of a purchaser shall be deemed to be waived and shall be without validity unless made in writing to the Galleries within ten days after the sale.

15. Neither the auctioneer nor any other representative of the Galleries shall have the authority to waive or alter, in whole or in part, any of these Conditions of Sale or except as provided in paragraphs 6 and 9 hereof, orally to cancel any sale.

Sales Conducted by

LOUIS J. MARION

WILLIAM A. SMYTH · THEODORE J. MULDOON
CHARLES A. HELLMICH · JOHN L. MARION

PARKE-BERNET GALLERIES · INC

LESLIE A. HYAM · *President*
LOUIS J. MARION · *Executive Vice-President*
MARY VANDEGRIFT · ROBERT F. METZDORF · *Vice-Presidents*
MAX BARTHOLET · *Secretary & Treasurer*

CATALOGUE

LIST OF ARTISTS

———————————————— ✳ ————————————————

NUMBER ONE
JACOB HUYSMANS
Portrait, Said to Be of a Lady of the Stuart Family

NUMBER TWO
FRANÇOIS CLOUET
Duc d'Alençon

NUMBER THREE
GIOVANNI BATTISTA MORONI
Marqués de Zúñiga y Requeséns

NUMBER FOUR
PIETRO DI DOMENICO
Madonna and Child with Two Angels

NUMBER FIVE
CORNEILLE DE LYON
Portrait of a Nobleman

NUMBER SIX
COSIMO ROSSELLI
Pietà

NUMBER SEVEN
GIOVANNI BELLINI
Madonna and Child

I

JACOB HUYSMANS FLEMISH: 1633-1680/90
1. *PORTRAIT, SAID TO BE OF A LADY OF THE STUART FAM-ILY*. Bust portrait to half-right of a young woman with dark brown ringlets straggling from under a lace-edged white cap; wearing a décolleté robe with scarlet *échelle* and yellow silk cloak, also trimmed with vandyked lace; dark brown background. *Cradled panel: 11½ x 9 inches*

> *Note:* This was formerly believed to be a portrait of Louisa Maria Theresa Stuart (1692-1712), the only surviving daughter of James II; but the costume is too early for this to be possible.

FRANÇOIS CLOUET FRENCH: C. 1510-1572
2. *DUC D'ALENÇON*. Bust portrait to half-right of a handsome young man with dark brown hair, wearing a rounded black hat with a white feather and a black doublet with frilled white ruff and a collar of pearls; dark gray backgound. *Cradled panel: 12½ x 9½ inches*

> The Duc d'Alençon (1554-1584) was the fourth son of Henri II and Catherine de Médicis; his three elder brothers succeeded to the throne as Francis II, Charles IX and Henri III, and his exclusion from the succession caused him to consider possible marriage with Queen Elizabeth of England. The present portrait must have been painted in the last years of Clouet's life, when the Duc was not yet twenty years of age.

Painted about 1571-72

Collection of the Comte de Montbrizon, Château de Saint Roch, France

From the Kleinberger Galleries, Inc., New York

[See illustration]

2

DUC D'ALENÇON

CLOUET

GIOVANNI BATTISTA MORONI   ITALIAN: C. 1520-1578

3. *MARQUES DE ZUNIGA Y REQUESENS*. Bust portrait to half-left, the eyes glancing toward the observer, of a handsome young man wearing a black velvet cap with jeweled band and high-necked black doublet with a white frilled ruff; greenish-gray background.   *25 x 18¼ inches*

Luis de Zúñiga y Requeséns (*c.*1522-1576) was Spanish Governor of the Netherlands under Philip II. His early career was as a government official and diplomatist, and in 1568 he became Lieutenant-General to Don John of Austria, whom he accompanied during the Lepanto campaign. He was appointed to the Governorship in Brussels in 1572, and remained there until his death.

An endorsement of the painting by Prof. Adolfo Venturi, dated Paris, May 19, 1928, will be given to the purchaser.

From the John Levy Galleries, New York

[See illustration]

MARQUES DE ZUNIGA Y REQUESENS

MORONI

PIETRO DI DOMENICO   SIENESE: 1457-1506

4. *MADONNA AND CHILD. WITH TWO ANGELS*. Three-quarter-length figure of the Virgin in red robe and hooded black cloak, holding the nude Child on her right hand, her left holding a spray of pinks, for which He is reaching, His right hand giving the benediction; behind her at left and right stand robed figures of angels with devout mien; gold background with *bulino*-work haloes.   *Cradled panel: 20¼ x 15 inches*

Collection of Captain R. Langton Douglas, London

Collection of Frank L. Babbott, Brooklyn, N.Y.

From the F. Kleinberger Galleries, Inc., New York

Loan Exhibition of Italian Primitives, Kleinberger Galleries, New York, 1917, no. 67, illus. in the catalogue

Recorded in Raimond van Marle, *The Development of the Italian Schools of Painting*, 1937, vol. XVI, p. 464

[See illustration]

MADONNA AND CHILD WITH TWO ANGELS

PIETRO DI DOMENICO

CORNEILLE DE LYON   FRENCH: C.1500-C1574

5. *PORTRAIT OF A NOBLEMAN*. Waist-length figure, glancing to the
observer, of a man with dark brown moustache and beard, wearing a round
black cap and black costume with broad bands of fur, frilled white lawn collar
and manchettes and holding a letter in his right hand; brilliant green background.   *Cradled panel: 10¾ x 7¼ inches*

[See illustration]

PORTRAIT OF A NOBLEMAN

CORNEILLE DE LYON

COSIMO ROSSELLI   FLORENTINE: 1439-1507

6. *PIETA*. Scene at the foot of the empty cross, against which a ladder is leaning. The body of Christ lies extended, His head on the lap of the Virgin, who wears a crimson robe and black hooded cloak; around them are a crowd of figures, including SS. John, Joseph of Arimathea, Nicodemus, Catherine and Sebastian, and other mourners, erect and kneeling; in the background are scattered edifices and a distant mountain landscape.

Cradled panel: 35 x 35 *inches*

Note: Cosimo Rosselli took part in the decoration of the Sistine Chapel in Rome for Pope Sixtus IV, and among his pupils and assistants were Piero di Cosimo and Fra Bartolommeo. Sir Joseph Duveen stated in a letter to Mr Cintas that the painting was originally bought by him upon the advice of Bernard Berenson.

Collection of Baron Lazzaroni, Paris

Collection of Sir Joseph Duveen, Bart., New York

From the John Levy Galleries, New York

[See illustration]

PIETA

COSIMO ROSSELLI

GIOVANNI BELLINI   VENETIAN: C. 1426-1516

7. *MADONNA AND CHILD*. Three-quarter-length seated figure to half-left of the youthful Virgin, clad in a crimson satin robe with dark blue hooded cloak and white wimple, holding on her right knee the seated nude Child, who grasps a bird in His right hand; background of green drapery opening to an extended landscape at left, with a solitary tree and a town in the distance.

Cradled panel: 32 x 26½ inches

Note: The painting is accompanied by endorsements from Dr. W. R. Valentiner, dated December 1, 1930; Dr. Detlev von Hadeln, dated Florence, March 20, 1931; and by Dr. Raimond van Marle. Von Hadeln describes the picture as having been painted by Bellini between 1490 and 1495, and states that Cima da Conegliano used the composition for a Madonna in the possession of Mr Tuck in Paris.

Dr. van Marle, in a lengthy monograph on the painting (*vide infra*), notes that the picture had been lost sight of for many years, since the Leuchtenberg collection was divided into two parts, one of which was taken to Russia by a descendant of the family, while the other part remained in Bavaria; he dates the picture from around the year 1500, or perhaps one or two years earlier. Prior to a long technical discussion of the work he remarks: "It is not at all difficult to establish the authorship of this delightful panel, the technical perfection of which, as well as the deep and serene sentiment which emanates from it, excludes all possibility of its being a work-shop production. Even those pictures executed under the master's direct supervision and perhaps in part from his own hand, a good many examples of which have come down to us, never reach this height of spiritual inspiration and masterful handling."

Painted about 1490-1500

Collection of the Duke of Leuchtenburg, Munich and St. Petersburg

From the John Levy Galleries, New York

Recorded in I. D. Passavant, *Gemäldesammlung seiner Kaiserl. Hoheit des Herzogs von Leuchtenberg*, 1851, no. 5

Described in Raimond van Marle, *The Development of the Italian Schools of Painting*, 1935, vol. XVII, pp. 318, 326

Described in Raimond van Marle, *A Madonna by Giovanni Bellini* (privately printed)

Engraved by I. N. Murel, 1851

[See photogravure]

MADONNA AND CHILD

BELLINI

NUMBER EIGHT

GIOVANNI BATTISTA MORONI

Portrait of a Young Woman

GIOVANNI BATTISTA MORONI   ITALIAN: C. 1520-1578

8. *PORTRAIT OF A YOUNG WOMAN*. Bust portrait to half-right, and glancing to the observer, of a young woman with plaited curly brown hair decked with pearls, wearing a tight-waisted brocaded mauve costume with slashed sleeves, starched white ruff and a golden neck chain; gray background.   *20 x 17 inches*

> *Note:* Dr. W. R. Valentiner, in a note dated Detroit, November 3, 1928, writes of this picture: "in my opinion, one of the finest female portraits known to me by *Giovanni Battista Moroni*, . . . the picture is in an unusually fine state of preservation, free from any repaint."

Collection of Prince Gagarin, St. Petersburg

From Böhler & Steinmayer, Lucerne

From the John Levy Galleries, New York

Recorded and illustrated in Davide Cugini, *Moroni Pittore*, 1939, p. 146, no. 83, fig. 18

[See photogravure]

PORTRAIT OF A YOUNG WOMAN

MORONI

NUMBER NINE
FERDINAND BOL
Portrait of a Man (The Burgomaster)

NUMBER TEN
FRANS HALS
The Merry Lute Player

NUMBER ELEVEN
SIR ANTHONY VAN DYCK
Mountjoy Blount, Earl of Newport and George, Lord Goring

NUMBER TWELVE
REMBRANDT HARMENSZ VAN RIJN
Portrait of a Young Girl, Said to be Hendrickje Stoffels

FERDINAND BOL   DUTCH: C. 1610-1680

9. *PORTRAIT OF A MAN (THE BURGOMASTER).* Half-length
portrait to half-right, and looking toward the observer, of a man with
moustache and chin beard, with long gray hair emerging from under a
broad-brimmed black hat, wearing black robes with white lawn collar and
holding a glove; seated in a chair with his left arm resting on a table covered
with an Oriental rug. Signed at upper left F. BOL, and dated 1659 on either
side of the escutcheon of the sitter.   *40 x 32½ inches*

Collection of Jules Porgès, Paris

From Moulton & Ricketts, London

Collection of C. G. Conn, Elkhart, Ind.

From the John Levy Galleries, New York

[See photogravure]

PORTRAIT OF A MAN (THE BURGOMASTER)

BOL

10. *THE MERRY LUTE PLAYER*. Half-length figure of a youth in black coat and doublet, the cuffs lined with blue, showing a white shirt at the neck, and wearing a black cap on the side of his tousled head; in his right hand he holds up a glass of wine towards which he looks with a smile; in his left hand he holds the neck of a lute, its striped body resting on a light grayish-green table. Shaded gray-green background lightening at upper right. Signed at lower right with monogram FH.   *Cradled panel: 35½ x 29½ inches*

> *Note:* Dr. W. R. Valentiner, in *Frans Hals Paintings in America* (*vide infra*), writes of the above painting: "One of the happiest inspirations of the artist painted with great bravura. It had popular success even at the time of its execution. . . . The motif is a further development of the composition of *A Cavalier and His Sweetheart*, . . . and shows the diagonal arrangement and the light and shadow contrasts still more strongly emphasized."
>
> Hofstede de Groot described it in vol. II of his *Catalogue Raisonné*, but in giving its history, gave the history of two paintings, the above and a later copy of the above, formerly in the collection of Sir Edgar Vincent, London. He corrected this error in the preface of his vol. IV (*vide infra*), and in the unpublished notes which are in the possession of the Ryksbureau voor Kunsthistorische Documentatie, The Hague.
>
> The model is the same as in the *Boy with a Skull* (the so-called 'Hamlet') in the Proby collection, London.

Painted in 1625-27

Collection Capello, Amsterdam, 1767, no. 28

Collection of Count Bonde, Stockholm

From M. Colnaghi, London

Collection of Jules Porgès, Paris

From Asher Wertheimer, London

Collection of Baron Ferdinand de Rothschild, Waddesdon Manor, Bucks.

Collection of Edmond Veil-Picard, Paris

From Gooden & Fox, London

From Duveen Bros., Inc., New York

Collection of John R. Thompson, Parke-Bernet Galleries, 1944

[Continued

Winter Exhibition of Old Masters, Royal Academy, London, 1891, no. 72

Exposition Hollandaise, Salle du Jeu de Paume des Tuileries, Paris, 1911, no. 55

Loan Exhibition of Dutch Paintings, Detroit Institute of Arts, Detroit, Mich., 1925, no. 4

Exhibition of Dutch Art, Royal Academy, Burlington House, London, 1929, no. 372

Century of Progress Exhibition of Paintings and Sculpture, Art Institute of Chicago, 1933, no. 62, illus. in the catalogue

Seventeenth Loan Exhibition of Old Masters, Detroit Institute of Arts, Detroit, Mich., 1935, no. 9, illus. in the catalogue

Twentieth Anniversary Exhibition, Official Art Exhibit of the Great Lakes Exposition, Cleveland Museum of Art, Cleveland, O., 1936, no. 219

Frans Hals Exhibition, Frans Hals Museum, Haarlem, 1937, no. 30, illus. in the catalogue

Exhibition of Masterpieces of Art, World's Fair, New York, 1940, no. 82

Exhibition of Paintings by the Great Dutch Masters of the Seventeenth Century, in Aid of the Queen Wilhelmina Fund, Duveen Galleries, New York, 1942, no. 14, illus. in the catalogue

Described in C. Hofstede de Groot, *Catalogue of the Works of the Most Eminent Dutch Painters*, 1910, vol. III, p. 23, no. 82.; and vol. IV, 1912, preface p. VI

Described and illustrated in Armand Dayot, *Grands & Petits Maîtres Hollandais*, 1912, p. 127, no. 57, illus. opp. p. 66

Recorded and illustrated in Wilhelm von Bode, *Frans Hals His Life and Work*, 1914, p. 32, no. 58 and pl. 25

Described and illustrated in W. R. Valentiner, *Frans Hals Des Meisters Gemälde (Klassiker der Kunst)*, 1923, p. 310, illus. p. 58

Described in H. Schneider and W. G. Constable, *Commemorative Catalogue of the Exhibition of Dutch Art, Paintings*, 1929, p. 54, no. 372, reproduced in the *Souvenir*, p. 31, no. 29

[*Continued*

THE MERRY LUTE PLAYER

HALS

Number 10—Concluded]

Illustrated in William Gibson, *The Dutch Exhibition at Burlington House*, in *Apollo*, Feb. 1929, vol. IX, p. 85

Illustrated in Arsène Alexandre, *L'Art Hollandais à La Royal Academy*, in *La Renaissance*, March 1929, vol. XII, p. 115

Described and illustrated in Alfred M. Frankfurter, *Paintings by Frans Hals in the United States*, in *The Antiquarian*, Sept. 1929, vol. 13, p. 84, illus..

Described and illustrated in Esther Singleton, *Old World Masters in New World Collections*, 1929, p. 224, illus. p. 223

Illustrated on the cover of *Parnassus*, Feb. 1935, vol. VII, no. II

Described and illustrated in W. R. Valentiner, *Frans Hals Paintings in America*, 1936, no. 20

Recorded in Walter Pach, *Catalogue of European & American Paintings, Masterpieces of Art*, 1940, p. 62, no. 82

Described and illustrated in N. S. Trivas, *The Paintings of Frans Hals*, 1941, p. 32, no. 27 and pl. 40

Described and illustrated in George Henry McCall and Prof. A. J. Barnouw, *Catalogue of Paintings by the Great Dutch Masters of the Seventeenth Century*, 1942, p. 31, no. 14, illus. p. 105

[See preceding photogravure]

SIR ANTHONY VAN DYCK   FLEMISH: 1599-1641

11. *MOUNTJOY BLOUNT, EARL OF NEWPORT AND GEORGE, LORD GORING.* Double portrait at half length: at left, a young man with long dark brown hair, wearing a cuirass with blue sash over a leather doublet and slashed rose and white costume, his left hand fondling his sword hilt, his left elbow resting on a stone ledge; at right is his friend standing in profile to left, with his head turned toward the observer, wearing a brown satin costume with cuirass and red shoulder scarf, his left hand resting on a staff; at left of the background wall, a glimpse of open landscape under a clouded sky.

48 x 57 inches

Mountjoy Blount, 1st Earl of Newport (1597-1666) was a natural son of Charles Blount, Earl of Devonshire and Penelope, Lady Rich, and was legitimized by their marriage in 1605; he was created Baron Mountjoy in 1618 and Earl of Newport in 1628, and in 1634 became Master of the King's Ordnance, taking part in the Civil War. After the Restoration, he retired to Oxford and died there in 1666.

George, Lord Goring (1608-1657), son of the Earl of Norwich and Mary, daughter of Lord Abergavenny, was a brilliant youth who in 1633 commanded as Colonel in the Dutch wars and was wounded at Breda in 1637; he became Governor of Portsmouth and a cavalry commander for the Royalists in the Civil War; in 1646 he was again in the Netherlands, commanding the English regiments in the Spanish service with the title of Colonel-General; he died in Madrid in 1657 in the habit of a Dominican friar, whence the provenience of the portrait (*vide infra*).

Note: Both of the friends were also painted separately by Van Dyck, the portrait of Goring being in the collection of the Earl of Clarendon, and the full-length portrait of the Earl of Newport in the Duveen collection.

Collection of the Marqués de Vatolla, Madrid

Collection Corredor, Madrid

Collection of Sir Joseph Duveen, Bart., New York

From Duveen Brothers, Inc., New York

Loan Exhibition of the Works of Van Dyck, Detroit Institute of Arts, Detroit, Mich., 1929, no. 45

Exhibition of Forty British Portraits, Duveen Galleries, New York, 1940, no. 4

Loan Exhibition, Milwaukee Art Institute, Milwaukee, Wis., 1946

[Continued

VAN DYCK *MOUNTJOY, EARL OF NEWPORT AND GEORGE, LORD GORING*

Number 11—Concluded]

Recorded and illustrated in W. R. Valentiner, *Paintings by Anthony Van Dyck* (*Eighth Loan Exhibition by Old Masters*), Detroit Institute of Arts, 1929, no. 45

Mentioned in the *Bulletin of the Detroit Institute of Arts*, 1929, p. X 91

Mentioned by W. R. Valentiner, *Die Van Dyck-Ausstellung in Detroit* in *Zeitschrift für bildende Kunst*, 1929, p. 111

Recorded and illustrated in Gustav Glück, *Van Dyck* (*Klassiker der Kunst*), 1931, no. 435

Mentioned in *Art News*, April 13, 1940; *Art Digest*, April 15, 1940; *Apollo*, June 1940, pp. 166-67; and *Connoisseur*, July 1940, pp. 28-29

[See preceding photogravure]

REMBRANDT HARMENSZ VAN RIJN   DUTCH: 1606-1669

12. *PORTRAIT OF A YOUNG GIRL, SAID TO BE HENDRICKJE STOFFELS*. Bust portrait, looking to the observer, of a young girl with curly fair hair gathered under a flanged and pleated brownish-red cap; wearing a matching costume with slashed front, a brown cloak draped over the right shoulder. Signed at right REMBRANDT, and dated 1651.   *23½ x 19½ inches*

> *Note:* The portrait was first described by Dr. Valentiner as probably of Hendrickje Stoffels. Hendrickje was a humble servant girl, who, three years after the death of Rembrandt's wife Saskia in 1642, took charge of his household, and became both his model and his mistress. She died between 1661 and 1663.

From Durand-Ruel, Paris

Collection of Charles H. Senff, New York, 1928

From F. Kleinberger, New York

Loan Exhibition of Paintings by Rembrandt, Detroit Institute of Arts, Detroit, Mich., 1930, no. 50

Exhibition, Masterpieces of Art, New York World's Fair, 1940, no. 88

Recorded in Hofstede de Groot, *Catalogue Raisonné of the Works of the Most Eminent Dutch Painters*, 1916, vol. VI, no 504

Recorded and illustrated in W. R. Valentiner, *Rembrandt, Wiedergefunde Gemälde (Klassiker der Kunst)*, 1921, no. 66, illus. pl. 63

Described and illustrated in W. R. Valentiner, *Rembrandt Paintings in America*, 1932, no. 111

Recorded in A. Bredius, *The Paintings of Rembrandt* (Phaidon Edition), n.d., no. 379

Recorded in Walter Pach, *Catalogue of European and American Paintings*, (Masterpieces of Art), New York, 1940, no. 88, p. 64

Recorded in Jakob Rosenberg, *Rembrandt* (Concordance of Paintings), 1948, p. 245

[See photogravure]

A YOUNG GIRL, SAID TO BE HENDRICKJE STOFFELS

REMBRANDT

NUMBER THIRTEEN
FRANS HALS
Colonel Aernout van Druyvesteyn

NUMBER FOURTEEN
REMBRANDT HARMENSZ VAN RIJN
Portrait of a Rabbi

NUMBER FIFTEEN
EL GRECO [DOMENICO THEOTOCOPULI]
The Annunciation

FRANS HALS   DUTCH: 1580-1666

13. *COLONEL AERNOUT VAN DRUYVESTEYN.* Waist-length
portrait to right and looking upwards, of a man with ruddy complexion,
tousled hair and fair moustache and beard, wearing black silk costume with a
huge starched white ruff, his left hand carried to his breast.

28½ x 24¼ inches

Note: Aernout Jansz van Druyvesteyn, the elder (1577-1627) was
Burgomaster of Haarlem, and appears in the same pose in *The Repast of the
Officers of Jorisdoelen at Haarlem,* the large group painting executed in 1627
now in the Frans Hals Museum in the same city. This is the only single portrait known which is directly connected with one of Hals's large group portraits, and Dr. Valentiner remarks of it: "It is hard to say whether this single
portrait is a first study of this masterpiece by Frans Hals, or has been executed afterwards by the artist on special commission from the sitter and then
given a more finished appearance through the addition of the left hand. The
great vivacity of expression and the spirited execution speaks for a first im-
pression in front of the model." It is probably identical with the painting described in Hofstede de Groot, no. 175 (*vide infra*), which passed through a
sale in Holland on August 10, 1785.

Trivas, *op. cit.,* no. 31B, lists the painting as a copy, citing unpublished
notes by Hofstede de Groot to the same effect, and mentioning the story that
it was sold by John G. Johnson because its authenticity was doubted. Dr.
Valentiner, however, in *Klassiker der Kunst,* stated unequivocally that he
considered this doubt not well grounded, and in his later brochure on the
painting, dated Detroit, March 4, 1926, which will be given to the purchaser,
refutes the story by stating: "The owner [Mr Johnson] in his interest in
adding another work of art to his collection, gave it in exchange—a trade
which he afterwards very much regretted himself, as he told me several times,
especially after it had become known how highly it was regarded by its next
possessor, Sir Hugh Lane."

Dr. Julius Held agrees with Dr. Valentiner's warm endorsement of
the painting.

Painted about 1627

Collection of John G. Johnson, Philadelphia, Pa.

From F. Kleinberger, Paris

Collection of Sir Hugh Lane, Bart., Director of the Dublin Museum

From Thomas Agnew & Sons, London

[Continued

COLONEL AERNOUT VAN DRUYVESTEYN

HALS

Number 13—Concluded]

Collection of Albert R. Jones, Kansas City, Mo.

From the John Levy Galleries, New York

Frans Hals Exhibition, Detroit Institute of Arts, Detroit, Mich., 1935, no. 8

Exhibition, Masterpieces of Art, World's Fair, New York, 1939, no. 176

Cf. C. Hofstede de Groot, *Catalogue Raisonné of the Works of the Most Eminent Dutch Painters*, 1910, vol. III, no. 175 (measurements slightly different)

Recorded and illustrated in W. R. Valentiner, *Frans Hals (Klassiker der Kunst)*, 1923, p. 62

Described and illustrated in W. R. Valentiner, *Frans Hals Paintings in America*, 1936, no. 19

Recorded in N. S. Trivas, *The Paintings of Frans Hals*, 1941, no 31B (see note, *supra*)

[See preceding photogravure]

REMBRANDT HARMENSZ VAN RIJN   DUTCH: 1606-1669

14. *PORTRAIT OF A RABBI.* Bust portrait to the observer of an elderly man with long flowing white beard, wearing a black velvet cap with a jeweled ornament and a gold chain over a gold-embroidered scarlet coat, his shoulders draped in a black cloak edged with fur.   *25 x 20¾ inches*

> *Note:* The history of this painting goes back to the great Leigh Court gallery of pictures, which was originally assembled by Philip Miles, a banker of Bristol, about 1816; the sale of the collection was at the instance of his grandson, Sir Philip Miles, Bart., in London in 1884, whence the present picture passed into the collection of Prince Demidoff. The portrait has been twice previously sold in America: in the collection of the traction magnate, Charles T. Yerkes (1910) and in the Ambrose Monell sale (1930).
>
> The painting is fully accepted by Bode, Hofstede de Groot and Valentiner, but Bredius (*vide infra*), indicates that it is doubted by certain authorities. Dr. Jakob Rosenberg, in his Concordance (*vide infra*), queries the ascription to Rembrandt, and is of the opinion that it is probably the work of Govaert Flinck.

Painted about 1635

Collection of Sir Philip Miles, Bart., Leigh Court, 1884

Collection of Prince Demidoff, Palazzo San Donato, Florence, 1885

Collection of Charles T. Yerkes, New York, 1910

Collection of Ambrose Monell, New Haven, Conn., and New York, 1930, no. 59

Loan Exhibition, Paintings by Rembrandt, Detroit Institute of Arts, Detroit, Mich., 1930, no. 10, illus. in the catalogue

Exhibition, Masterpieces of Art, World's Fair, New York, 1940, no. 88A, illus. in the catalogue

Recorded and illustrated in W. von Bode, *Complete Work of Rembrandt,* 1899, vol. III, no. 202

Recorded in Adolphe Rosenberg, *The Work of Rembrandt,* p. 189

Recorded in Eugène Dutuit, *Catalogue Historique et Descriptif des Tableaux et Dessins de Rembrandt,* 1885, p. 47

[Continued

PORTRAIT OF A RABBI

REMBRANDT

Number 14—Concluded]

Recorded and illustrated in Rosenberg and Valentiner, *Rembrandt* (*Klassiker der Kunst*), 1908, p. 187

Recorded in C. Hofstede de Groot, *Catalogue Raisonné of the Works of the Most Eminent Dutch Painters: Rembrandt*, 1916, vol. VI, no. 409

Described and illustrated in W. R. Valentiner, *Rembrandt Paintings in America*, 1932, no. 57

Recorded in Jakob Rosenberg, *Rembrandt* (Concordance of Paintings), 1948, p. 243 (see note, *supra*)

Recorded in A. Bredius, *The Paintings of Rembrandt* (Phaidon Edition), n.d., p. 12, no. 209 (see note, *supra*)

Engraved by J. Young, 1822

[See preceding photogravure]

EL GRECO [DOMENICO THEOTOCOPULI]

SPANISH: C. 1541-1614

15. *THE ANNUNCIATION.* At left is the figure of the Virgin in purplish-red robe, green cloak and lace mantilla, kneeling at a *prie-dieu* with her left hand on an open missal; looking upward to the right towards the Angel with spread wings and golden yellow robe, holding a stem of lilies and gesturing with the right hand; between them is the Holy Ghost in the form of a white dove. On the parapet below are a work-basket and a vase of tulips.

39½ x 27 inches

Note: The above painting, which is accepted by Cossío, August Mayer, Legendre and Hartmann, and Aznar, is given in Wethey's controversial *catalogue raisonné* (*vide infra*), to El Greco's son, Jorge Manuel; but Professor Wethey had seen only a photograph of the painting at the time that the entry was made.

The prototype of this composition is in the Toledo Museum, Toledo, O.; one of the two came originally from the collection of Fabricio Potestad, Madrid, although Wethey is ambiguous on this point. Cossío dates the present picture 1594-1604, Mayer and Aznar, 1605-12.

Collection of Fabricio Potestad, Madrid (see note, *supra*)

Collection of Mrs Horace Schmidlapp, Cincinnati, O.

Recorded in Manuel B. Cossío, *El Greco,* 1908, vol. I, p. 573, no. 125

Recorded and illustrated in August L. Mayer, *El Greco,* 1926, pp. 3-4, no. 9A

Recorded in Legendre and Hartmann, *El Greco,* 1937, no. 103

Recorded and illustrated in Camón Aznar, *Dominico Greco,* 1950, vol. II, p. 1358, no. 37, fig. 579

Recorded and illustrated in Harold E. Wethey, *El Greco and His School,* 1962, no. X-17, p. 169, fig. 173 (see note, *supra*)

[See photogravure]

THE ANNUNCIATION

EL GRECO

NUMBER SIXTEEN
ANGELO ALLORI [BRONZINO]
Portrait of a Lady with a Book

NUMBER SEVENTEEN
PETER PAUL RUBENS AND ATELIER
The Woman Taken in Adultery

NUMBER EIGHTEEN
DUTCH MASTER, CLOSE TO HALS
The Cavalier

NUMBER NINETEEN
LUCA GIORDANO
The Virgin of the Immaculate Conception, after Murillo

NUMBER TWENTY
SIR ANTHONY VAN DYCK [ATELIER OF]
Charles II as Prince of Wales

NUMBER TWENTY-ONE
MARIE LOUISE ELIZABETH VIGÉE-LEBRUN
Portrait of Princess Tufialkin

47

ANGELO ALLORI [BRONZINO]　　　　　ITALIAN: 1502-1572

16. *PORTRAIT OF A LADY WITH A BOOK.* Waist-length portrait to half-left of a lady in a tight-waisted green robe with slashed and puffed black sleeves and gold lace yoke, wearing a Juliet cap, necklace and gold chain; holding a pair of gloves, and in her left hand an open book.

Cradled panel: 35 x 27 inches

Note: The subject is a lady of the Medici court of the time of Cosimo I. The picture is accompanied by an endorsement by Professor Adolfo Venturi, dated Paris, June 12, 1927.

Collection of Baron Lazzaroni, Paris

From the John Levy Galleries, New York

[See illustration]

PORTRAIT OF A LADY WITH A BOOK

BRONZINO

PETER PAUL RUBENS and Atelier   FLEMISH: 1577-1640

17. *THE WOMAN TAKEN IN ADULTERY.* (John VIII: 3-11.) The scene is crowded with figures painted at half-length: at the left, the Saviour in scarlet robe and gray cloak stands in profile to the right with His hands outstretched, facing the weeping woman, who wears a greenish-black robe with headveil, and the group of her accusers; among whom are a bald-headed old man with a beard, a helmeted soldier, several curious youths, an elderly man in an ermine-trimmed scarlet robe leaning on a staff, and at right the High Priest wearing greenish-blue robes and golden mantle, a banderole inscribed in Hebrew across his forehead; in the background are a column at the left, and a stone embrasure with a tomb at upper right.

Cradled panel: 40¼ x 54¼ inches

Note: This painting is a replica of the one in the Royal Museum, Brussels (*Klassiker der Kunst,* p. 54), which originally came from the collection of Sir Philip Miles, Bart., at Leigh Court, Bristol. John Smith in his *Catalogue Raisonné* of 1830 (vol. II, no. 796), credited the picture now at Brussels to be the one known by tradition to have been painted for the family of Knuyf (Knyff) in Antwerp and sold by Canon Knyff in 1785; but it seems likely that neither the Brussels painting nor the present picture is identical with the Knyff group. It may be of interest to note that according to the *Antwerpsche Archivenblad,* vol. II, p. 83, Rubens in his testament bequeathed under no. 41 of his inventory a painting of *The Woman Taken in Adultery* to one Gieles Sprincen, the fate of which is unknown.

Max Rooses in the *Annales* (*vide infra*), writes of the present picture in part as follows "Entirely from the hand of Rubens, but less finished than the Brussels picture. Rubens left his work without adding the final glazings, . . . the execution is freer than that of the picture of 1612." In a monograph by Maurice W. Brockwell, dated Feb. 20, 1919, which will be given to the purchaser, he sets forth at length the history and details of this work and the Brussels painting, and quotes the opinion of M. Pol de Mont, Director of the Musée Royal, Antwerp, to the effect that the present picture "is absolutely and entirely by Rubens." De Mont adds that Dr. Max Rooses, having seen the picture in May 1907, confirmed his opinion in the following words: ". . . this work was painted by Rubens; that fact admits of no doubt whatever. . . . Only he did not give it the final touches."

Dr. Julius Held is of the opinion that the painting is by Rubens with the assistance of the atelier.

Painted about 1612-13

[*Continued*

RUBENS AND ATELIER *THE WOMAN TAKEN IN ADULTERY*

Number 17—Concluded]

Collection of Adolphe Schuster, Vienna and Brussels

Collection Curty, Vienna

From the F. Kleinberger Galleries, Inc., New York (*as by* Rubens)

Exhibited at the Antwerp Museum, Antwerp, 1908

Exposition de L'Art Belge au XVIIme Siècle, Palais du Cinquantenaire, Brussels, 1910 (not in catalogue)

Inaugural Exhibition, Toledo Art Museum, Toledo O., 1912, no. 207, illus. in the catalogue (*as by* Rubens)

Exhibited at the Cincinnati Art Museum, Cincinnati, O., 1914

Exhibition of Paintings and Drawings by Peter Paul Rubens, Detroit Institute of Arts, Detroit, Mich., 1936, no. 3 (*as by* Rubens)

Described by Max Rooses in *Annales* of the *Bulletin Rubens,* 1910, vol. v, no. 256 *bis,* pp. 291-92 (*vide supra*)

Recorded in W. R. Valentiner, *Catalogue of an Exhibition of Sixty Paintings and Some Drawings by Peter Paul Rubens,* Detroit, Mich., 1936, no. 3 (*as by* Rubens)

[See preceding photogravure]

DUTCH MASTER, CLOSE TO HALS   CIRCA 1610

18. *THE CAVALIER.* Bust portrait to half-right of a man with sparse hair, auburn moustache and beard, wearing a black costume with a starched white ruff; greenish-brown background.   *Cradled panel: 18 x 14¾ inches*

> *Note:* Dr. W. R. Valentiner, in a holograph note dated 1921, on the back of a photograph of this painting, states that he believes this to be an early work of Hals, painted about 1610-12, and compares it with the portrait of *Jacobus Zaffius,* dated 1611, and two other portraits of the same period in Frankfurt and London; appending a technical analysis of the painting.

Collection of Dr. John E. Stillwell, New York, 1927 (*as by* Frans Hals)

[See illustration]

THE CAVALIER

DUTCH MASTER

LUCA GIORDANO   ITALIAN: 1632-1705

19. *THE VIRGIN OF THE IMMACULATE CONCEPTION, AFTER MURILLO.* The Virgin in white robe and blue cloak, her hands clasped to her breast and with an aureole of stars above her head, stands on a crescent moon crushing the head of the serpent of Evil, supported by a white cloud. Around her are innumerable naked cherubs with lilies, bay leaves, sprigs of flowers and a mirror; other hordes of cherubim in the skies above. Signed at lower centre LUCAS JORDANUS, and dated 1682.   *79 x 59 inches*

Note: Murillo's famous composition, which is the prototype of the present picture, exists in several versions, the most famous being the one in the Prado, Madrid.

[See illustration]

THE VIRGIN OF THE IMMACULATE CONCEPTION

LUCA GIORDANO

SIR ANTHONY VAN DYCK [Atelier of]   Flemish: 1599-1641

20. *CHARLES II AS PRINCE OF WALES*. Full-length figure to half-left and looking towards the observer, of the young prince with long dark brown curls, wearing a gold-brocaded slashed and puffed rose red costume with leather doublet, sword, and vandyked lawn collar; his right hand resting on a staff, his left holding a black hat with a white plume.   64 x 43¼ *inches*

Note: Frank T. Sabin contributed the following information concerning the painting: "The picture comes from the Earl of Harrington, and its history is that it has remained in the family for generations, and was probably painted for an ancestor, Catherine Countess of Chesterfield, who was governness of the Royal Children. Vandyke [*sic*] himself proposed to her, but was refused. She married Henry Lord Stanhope, a son and heir of Philip 1st Lord Chesterfield. . . . [It] is probably the last portrait painted by Vandyke, remained in the Stanhope family, and became the property of the branch that became Earls of Harrington.

"The picture was engraved T.Q.L. by Wenceslaus Hollar, who was drawing master to the Prince of Wales, at Antwerp in 1649. He has introduced a characteristic Hollaresque view of Buckingham House in the left corner background. Also engraved by a contemporary French engraver in line, with a hunting scene added in the background, and by an anonymous English engraver of the period as an oval, plain background. The only other portrait of the Prince by Vandyke apart from group portraits of the Royal family, is the full-length at Windsor, representing him at the age of 5 or 6 years, in a suit of armour. . . ."

Painted about 1641, probably for Catherine, Countess of Chesterfield

Collection of the Earl of Harrington, Elvaston Castle, Derby

From Frank T. Sabin, London (*as by* Van Dyck)

Engraved in line by Wenceslaus Hollar, Antwerp, 1649

Engraved in line (oval) by an anonymous British engraver (Brit. Mus. cat. 1908, vol. 1, p. 395, no. 6)

[See illustration]

CHARLES II AS PRINCE OF WALES

ATELIER OF VAN DYCK

MARIE LOUISE ELIZABETH VIGEE-LEBRUN

FRENCH: 1755-1842

21. *PORTRAIT OF PRINCESS TUFIALKIN*. Half-length figure of a beautiful young girl with tousled auburn hair flowing over her right shoulder and tied with a scarlet bandeau; she wears a loose pleated white lawn robe partly covered by a scarlet cloak tied with a cord at the waist, the upper half of her left arm bare; blue sky background. Signed at lower left illegibly, and dated in Russian *Moscow*, 1800. *25 x 21¾ inches*

> *Note*: According to Helm (*vide infra*), the artist painted the head of her subject in Moscow and completed the picture in Paris after the Revolution; but the date on the painting would seem to refute this, since Mme. Lebrun was in St. Petersburg from 1789-1800 continuously.

Collection A. Couteaux, Paris, 1863

Collection of Boris Serguyev

From Wildenstein & Co., Inc., New York

Exhibited at the Cleveland Museum of Art, Cleveland, O.

Recorded in *Souvenirs de Mme. Vigée-Lebrun; Catalogue de Ses Oeuvres*, p. 274

Recorded in W. H. Helm, *Vigée-Lebrun, Her Life, Works and Friendships*, n.d., p. 223

[See photogravure]

PRINCESS TUFIALKIN

VIGEE-LEBRUN

NUMBER TWENTY-TWO
GILBERT STUART
John Shaw

NUMBER TWENTY-THREE
THOMAS SULLY
George Washington, after Stuart

NUMBER TWENTY-FOUR
GEORGE BELLOWS
The Skeleton

22. *JOHN SHAW*. A man with ruddy complexion and powdered white hair, seen at waist-length seated to half-left in a red armchair and before a red drapery; wearing a blue velvet coat with brass buttons, buff vest and white stock, and with the fingers of his left hand thrust into a book.

36 x 28½ inches

Note: John Shaw (1750-1820) was a New York financier, a wine merchant and merchant-fleet owner. He was a lineal descendant of Wouter Van Twiller, Dutch Governor of New York, and married Mrs Steel, the widow of a British army officer. The painting was inherited by the sitter's daughter, Alice Long Shaw (*vide infra*) descending in the family for several generations. This portrait was loaned to Washington and Lee University at Lexington, Virginia, in 1923, and hung there in the Carnegie Library for several years.

A second portrait of John Shaw by Gilbert Stuart was presented some years ago by Mr R. Stevenson Scott to the National Gallery of Ireland, to mark the visit of the then President Cosgrave to New York.

Painted in New York in 1793

Collection of Alice Long Shaw (Mrs John Edward Foley), New York, daughter of the sitter

Collection of Arthur Morgan Foley, her son

Collection of Henry Baretta Foley, his son

Collection of Elodie Foley (Mrs Lawrence H. Pugh), Thibodaux, La., his daughter

From the Ehrich Galleries, New York

Exhibited at Washington and Lee University, Lexington, Va.

Described and illustrated in Lawrence Park, *Gilbert Stuart,* 1926, vol. II, p. 677-8, no. 749, ill. vol. IV, pl. 459, no. 749

[See illustration]

JOHN SHAW

GILBERT STUART

THOMAS SULLY   AMERICAN: 1783-1872

23. *GEORGE WASHINGTON, AFTER STUART*. Bust portrait, of the
Stuart 'Atheneum' type, slightly to left, with powdered hair; wearing black
coat with high collar, black vest and lace jabot; light brownish background.

30 x 25 inches

Collection of John R. Thompson, Parke-Bernet Galleries, 1944

[See illustration]

GEORGE WASHINGTON, AFTER STUART

SULLY

BELLOWS   *THE SKELETON*

GEORGE BELLOWS   AMERICAN: 1882-1925

24. *THE SKELETON*. View of a seashore with high rounded green hills under a stormy dark blue sky, a village at left in the distance; in the central foreground is the huge skeleton hull of an uncompleted ship. Two men in a small rowing boat are pulling towards the shore over a choppy dark sea. Signed at lower right GEO. BELLOWS, and signed and titled on back of canvas.

$29\frac{1}{2}$ x $44\frac{1}{2}$ *inches*

Painted in 1916

Collection of Steven C. Clark, New York

From M. Knoedler & Co., Inc., New York

Tenth Annual Arizona Art Exhibition, Arizona State Fair, Phoenix, Ariz., 1924, no. 6

Illustrated in *International Studio,* Aug. 1920, pl. XXIII

Illustrated in Emma Bellows, *The Paintings of George Bellows,* 1929, pl. 61

[See illustration]

[END OF SALE]

$\mathcal{PB}$

PARKE-BERNET GALLERIES • INC
designs its catalogues and directs
all details of illustration, text
and typography

PRINTED IN THE U.S.A. BY
PUBLISHERS PRINTING-ROGERS KELLOGG CORPORATION
NEW YORK